Room on the Broom

Colouring Book

Coloured in by:

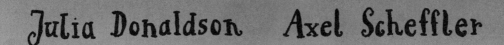

....

Julia Donaldson   Axel Scheffler

MACMILLAN CHILDREN'S BOOKS

Hello, Witch!

The witch had a cat and a very tall hat,
And long ginger hair which she wore in a plait.

The Witch Has Lost Her Hat

Can you draw it on her head and colour her in?
Try designing some other hats for her to wear!

Would she suit a pirate hat?

Drawing and Colouring

Follow the outlines to complete each picture - then colour them in!

A New Look for the Witch

Use your colouring pencils to give the witch a new outfit.

You can use collage paper too!

The Stormy Wind Blew

Over the reeds and the rivers they flew.
The bird shrieked with glee and the stormy wind blew.

Can you colour the picture and draw in lots of rain?

Fill in the Missing Letters

Do you know who all these characters are?
Write in the missing letters and colour the pictures.

w i t c h

b i r d

c a t

f r o g

d o g

Look Out!

A fire-breathing dragon is chasing the witch.

Draw some flames coming out of his mouth and colour him in.

Copy and Colour

Use the grid to help you copy the picture, then colour it in!

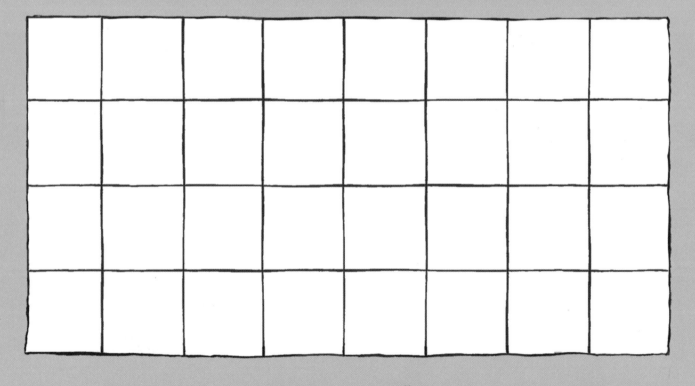

Drawing and Colouring

Follow the outlines to complete each picture - then colour them in!

Muddy Colouring

Use your best brown crayon to cover the animals with
mud and transform them into a horrible beast.

He Started to Shake!

Colour in this picture of the scared dragon.

Join the Dots

Who's throwing things into the cauldron? Join the dots to find out.

Colour the Clothes
Here are all the witch's things. Can you colour them in?

Creature Colouring

Colour in the happy animals.

Complete the pictures and
colour them in!

Can You Draw a Dragon?

Use the grid to help you copy
the picture, then colour it in.

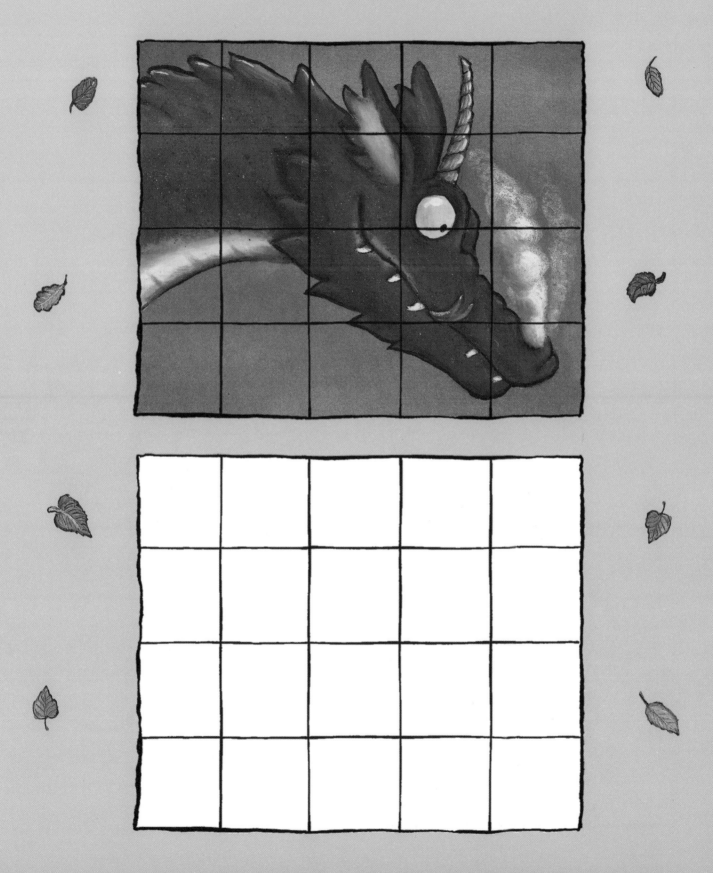

A Truly Magnificent Broom

With seats for the witch and the cat and the dog,
A nest for the bird and a shower for the frog.

Picture Crossword

Use the picture clues to help you fill in the puzzle.